XTIGONE

A contemporary lyrical re-imagining
based on Sophicles' *Antigone* by
Nambi E. Kelley

www.youthplays.com
info@youthplays.com
424-703-5315

COPYRIGHT RULES TO REMEMBER

CAST OF CHARACTERS

TIGS, a young woman in her late teens with a warrior's soul.

MARCELLUS, a gentleman of 60, the mayor, uncle to Tigs, father to Beau.

TEA FLAKE, a musical young woman of 20, speechwriter, fierce yet tender-hearted.

FAY, a lady of 60, dutiful and seemingly passive, wife to Marcellus, aunt to Tigs.

E-MEM, a young man of 20, gang leader with a sincere heart of gold.

CHORUS 1, a young woman in her 20s, dancer, musically inclined, plays IZZY and CHOCOLATE BOY.

CHORUS 2, an elderly lady, dancer, musically inclined, plays OLD BLIND WOMAN and SPIRIT.

CHORUS 3, a man in his 20s, dancer, musically inclined, plays LE ROI and ERNESTO.

CHORUS 4, a man in his 20s, dancer, musically inclined, plays BEAU and BRACE.

Chorus takes on the characters of various miscellaneous roles throughout the play, including the warring gangs, citizens, etc. Except for the specific chorus breakdowns listed above, delineation of chorus parts is at the discretion of the director. This play is designed for a cast of nine, but can be executed with more or fewer chorus actors if desired.

SETTING

A present day city that is held hostage by children and men with guns.

ACKNOWLEDGEMENTS

Xtigone was developed under the tutelage of Pulitzer Prize winner Lynn Nottage, LaMaMa International Symposium for Playwrights, Spoleto, Italy.

Xtigone premiered on February 14, 2015, at The African American Shakespeare Company in San Francisco, under the leadership of Artistic Director L. Peter Callender and Founder and Executive Director Sherri Young, with the following cast and production team:

CAST

TIGS	Ryan Nicole Austin
MARCELLUS DA MAYOR	Dwight Dean Mahabir
FAY	Jasmine Strange
BEAU	Michael Wayne Turner
E-MEM	AeJay Mitchell
ERNESTO	Drew Watkins
TEA FLAKE	Naima Shalhoub
IZZY	Tavia Percia
LE ROI	Howard Johnson
OLD BLIND WOMAN/SPIRIT	Awele Makeba
CHOCOLATE BOY/CHORUS	Wilgens Pierre
YOUNG GANGSTA/CHORUS	Cadence Crawley-Strange
CHORUS	Brooklyn Fields

PRODUCTION TEAM

Director, Rhodessa Jones; Musical Composer, Tommy "Emcee Soulati" Shepherd; Stage Manager, Hannah Westbrook; Technical Director, Kevin Myrick; Lighting Designer, Kevin Myrick; Scenic Design, Bert van Aalsburg; Costume Designer, Katherine Nowacki; Sound Design, Jamal Parson with Project Level; Running Crew, Storm White, Fe'Lisha Goodlow.

PLAYWRIGHT'S NOTES ON STYLE

On Casting: As this play is heavily influenced by music, all the actors need to have musical abilities, whether it be vocal or instrumental, and should be comfortable moving in their bodies in a range of dance styles. Although moments in the text are race specific, this play can and should be performed with a multi-ethnic cast.

On Music: The language of the play is intended to be performed in conjunction with live music. Text in ALL CAPS is intended to be sung. The music should be specific to hip hop and Latin music styles as representative of the warring gangs, but should range in style from hip hop to opera and any style to be imagined by the creative team involved, including jazz, blues, spoken word, country, etc., to represent the voices of the community in the play.

On Movement: The choreography of the play is intended to be continuously expressed thru the chorus and the character of Spirit. Choreographic elements range from hip hop dance to ballet and every dance style imaginable as dictated by the emotional truth of the scene and as imagined by the creative team.

On Chorus: The warring gang factions are divided as follows: Chocolate Boy is a *"(Dis)Sciple Gangsta"* and E-Mem is their leader. Brace is a *Latin King*, and Ernesto is their leader. Spirit is the gatekeeper of ritual who travels to a burial site to return lost souls home to their respective religious creators. Her body should be graceful, her voice, melodic of heaven. She takes on the physical presence of the Old Blind Woman in order to help facilitate creating peace in the world of these characters.

DEDICATION

For all the children who've been aborted by gun violence.

PROLOGUE

(TEA FLAKE, the chorus leader, enters The Square before a gathering crowd of the CHORUS, made up of warring gangs and community members. Music ensues. TIGS and BEAU embrace overlooking The Square. Music continues.)

BEAU: Tigs, where's E-Mem? Rally's to start soon.

TIGS: Beau, you know my brother ain't gonna miss. Say he finally gonna get his Disciple Gangstas to call that gun truce today.

BEAU: With Ernesto's Latin Kings? Yeah right. No disrespect, but if E-Mem on the real for a truce, why he runnin' a gang?

TIGS: He say you make change for the better from the inside.

BEAU: He *say*.

TIGS: ...I believe 'em.

(She avoids Beau's eyes.)

BEAU: Then why you cryin' — ?

(E-Mem appears in her memory —)

E-MEM: Anything happen to me at this rally — be like Emmett Till's mama and show folks what they did to my face —

E-MEM/BEAU: — Don't cry —

TIGS: — Ain't cryin', Beau.

E-MEM: Like the folks in Liberia followed Mamie's lead unburying their dead leavin' them on the steps of the U.S. Embassy —

TIGS: Ain't nothin' wrong, Beau —

E-MEM: South African mamas unburying their children. Leaving them in the streets to get folks to face HIV —

TIGS: I'm good, Beau!

E-MEM: You want the truth to be buried? Or you want the truth to be known? Unearth the truth!

TIGS: I said I'm good!

E-MEM: Unearth the truth!

BEAU: Girl. Give me that face.

(Beau cradles her face with his hands.)

My kiss is my promise. When we get married, you won't have to worry about none of this stuff no more. You can even quit yo' job at that school —

TIGS: Won't quit. Love them babies —

BEAU: Shut up woman, I'm working! ...That's one kiss.

(He kisses her once.)

...I'ma buy you a house, that's two kisses —

TIGS: Now how you gonna —?!

(She starts to respond, stops herself.)

BEAU: Uh huh, sho you right to hush them lips.

(He kisses her twice.)

— And we gon' fill it with our own pretty babies and live in the happily ever after. That's three, NO, four kisses —

(He smothers her with kisses, she laughs.)

TIGS: Your little peach fuzz tickles!

BEAU: Peach fuzz my ass! I'm a man! ...Wanna play X-box?

TIGS: That ain't the real! You silly, Beau!

BEAU: Beau. Now see that? My name's Beau. I'm your beau, *and* your boo. How much realer can it be?

(E-Mem in Tig's memory —)

E-MEM: Even if it means you die for what you believe, Sis, you unearth the truth.

TIGS: What E-Mem's fightin' for—

E-MEM: Unearth the truth! And then...thank the ancestors for a job well done.

TIGS: —Unearth the truth, thank the ancestors—

BEAU: How you gon' do all that?

TIGS: Yeah, ain't nobody got time for that. But E-Mem say that's the real. There's E-Mem! Time for the meeting.

(Lights changes as music continues as –)

SCENE 1

(Jazz/Blues music fills The Square.)

TEA FLAKE: WELCOME TO THE CITY
HOME OF THE GRAVE
SLAVE OPPRESSION
WINTER IN SESSION
"PEOPLE" VERSUS "FOLKS"
GANG WARRIN' IN THE MAZE.

(Enter MARCELLUS as cameras flash.)

THE LAND OF MARCELLUS—
KNOWN TO HIM AS "OZ"
NOWHERE OVER THE RAINBOW
TRUTH BLOODIED IN GAUZE.
IT'S CAUSE?
HIS HONOR MARCELLUS VERSUS HIS NEPHEWS' GANGS
ERNESTO AND E-MEM BARING FANGS—

(The GANGS begin an elaborate step rifle drill, like rebel soldiers in a Third World country.)

SPRANG

FROM THE THIN LINE BETWEEN LOVE AND HATE
NOW THE TOWN'S A WAR ZONE
KILLIN' DOMINATES
HIV
PO-LICE BRUTALITY
STILL RULIN' IN THE HOOD
STILL RULIN' ME

(E-Mem and ERNESTO enter The Square.)

CHORUS: GUNS

TEA FLAKE: IN EVERY CORNER IN EVERY HAND

CHORUS: GUNS

TEA FLAKE: SPILLIN' BLOOD 'CROSS MAMA GOD'S LAND

CHORUS: GUNS

TEA FLAKE: HELD BY CHILDREN WITH NO MOTHERS NO FATHERS

CHORUS: GUNS

TEA FLAKE: TRIGGERS PULLED BY OUR SONS AND DAUGHTERS

CHORUS: GUNS

TEA FLAKE: KILLIN' BABIES DAUGHTERS SONS

CHORUS: GUNS

E-MEM: MAKING MONEY FOR SOMEONE...

TIGS: BUT WHO?

TEA FLAKE: AND TIGGY?
SHE JUST LIKE US
SEARCHIN' SINCE ANTIQUITY
FOR HER HEART'S VIRGINITY.

CRÈME DA CREAM
OF HER DEAR OLD DADDY'S DREAM.
THE DREAM OF THE DEAD
INSTEAD
OVER HER HEAD
IN THIS CITY STYLE WAR.
AND WHAT WILL HER FIGHT BE?

(A car screech. An explosion of gunfire.)

(Bam! Bam! Bam! Bam!)

Drive by! Everybody get down!

(Chaos! Screams!)

(At last, the gunfire subsides. Ernesto and E-Mem. Dead.)

(Shoes of the two fallen boys lay in chalk outlines where their bodies once were. Gun smoke rises from their shoes.)

(Sirens. Of the Greek kind.)

(Descending from the sky is SPIRIT, draped in white.)

OLD BLIND WOMAN: I feel her. Spirit is here.

(Spirit hums, sprinkling holy water and dirt over the fallen shoes as −)

(A flurry of texts & Twitter tweets −)

CHORUS: *(Twitter & text messages:)* "E-MEM SHOT DEAD!" "YOU HEAR?" "ERNESTO!" "NO!" "OMG!" "WTF?"

(Text messages fly as −)

SCENE 2

(Tigs and IZZY cradle the bodies of their dead brothers, E-Mem and Ernesto, as their spirits look on.)

E-MEM: Is that us?

ERNESTO: Is that me?

TIGS: Sister Izzy
In a tizzy is my heart and head
Sister girl have you seen
That both of our dear brothers is dead?

E-MEM: Dead?

ERNESTO: Oh man.

IZZY: A Latin King versus a Gangsta 'Sciple

Got drive-by killed in the madness of the rival.

E-MEM: You had me drive-byed, man?

ERNESTO: You had **me** *drive-byed!*

E-MEM: Man you dumb!

ERNESTO: Hey, hermano, it wasn't me!

TIGS: I seen the deed
Seen them bleed
And my heart is heavy
Makes me think of ol' Katrina
When hydro broke them levees.

IZZY: Cuz your head is hurting, pounding tired
Our bros were fired from this job of life
Strife
Has us ilked and strained
To see sunlight.

TIGS: It ain't bright, don't look too hard
It's in our own front yard
This ain't a horror-cane or twister
In some other "Land of Oz" my sister
City's Mayor, our Uncle, is on the fat.

E-MEM: Marcellus the true gangsta!

ERNESTO: Marcellus the next gov'nor!

E-MEM: Gangsta makin' mad loot off puttin' guns in our kids' hands! Gov'nor, psh!

ERNESTO: Don't hate cuz he like me more than you, hombre.

E-MEM: See? Dumb!

TIGS: Folks all over the 'net
Bloggin' tweetin' facebookin'
Marcellus gonna say to the press
It is best to leave both brothers neatly dressed.
Buried with honor
No dishonor
Like the sons and daughters of the gun
Left buried 'neath this city's sun
Their truth unheard
In-jured
Stolen lives from their "unfinished reach"
Their voices of dim
Cherubic voices of the murdered dead
Ain't neva gon' begin
To Win
Nor choose to lose
Just snooze
In the forever of emptied shoes
Like the babies of the Holocaust
Lost
In the abyss of Adolf's diss.

IZZY: So how little ol' you gon' fix big ol' this?

TIGS: Sis.
We gotta leave Ernesto
In the ground below
Keep him covered
Smothered
In his truth cuz shouldn't nothin' be honored

ERNESTO: What I do? I deserve honor!

E-MEM: Shoulda signed the gun truce 'stead o' havin' me shot, that'd be your honor!

ERNESTO: I tol' you, hermano, it wasn't me!

E-MEM: If not you, then who?

TIGS: But we gotta un-bury E-Mem

Cuz in him was the very best of men

E-MEM: Yes! Leave me UN-buried, that is my honor!

TIGS: Leave him to lay
In the way
Of street cleaners
Be left to pigeon birds
Who ain't heard
The Word
That his flesh been messed.
We should let him rot down on Wabash
For all the hunks and punks
And queers to sneer
Be near
To the rats
And the fats
Of the homeless
Which ain't less.
This, our fair city, Chicago
Founded by da Black man Du Sable [DU-SAH-BULL]
Has got to move beyond pity
Bare
And smell the rotting wear and tear
Of our brother
For all others
To see that this be what happens

When the gun of dis-ease
Contracts, then eases...
Will you help me un-bury our brother E?

IZZY: Un-bury?

TIGS: Yes! Like E-Mem say—
—Said
UN-cover the dead
UN-cover our truths
Like Mamie Till
Or the rebels of Liberia
Rotting flesh the criteria
For change.

ERNESTO: That's deep! ...I think.

E-MEM: Don't think. Gives you wrinkles.

ERNESTO: Really? Oh man.

TIGS: Un-bury this young Black warrior
Who came
From the same
Womb-man
As you and me.

IZZY: E-Mem wasn't no "young black warrior"
No Malcolm X or Emmett Till
No Martin or a Luther or a King
He was a punk whose pants was always outright
Baggy
Talkin' smack with gold teeth chatting
Smokin' dope
On a rope hangin' right-side down outta trees
Hootin' and hollerin' about "the m-a-n"
Not givin' him a j-o-b
All he ever had to do was just pick up a book

And not look
Like he was raised on dis-ease.

E-MEM: Izzy sound like tabloid TV!

TIGS: Don't tell me you believe the hype?

IZZY: You think Anderson Cooper should *CNN Heroes* him tonight?

TIGS: What kinda sister are you?

IZZY: I'm real
Before Pops died
He said our brothers were cursed —

IZZY & TIGS: "Black men raised only by Black women
Exeunt only by hearse"

TIGS: Mama did her best —

IZZY: OD-ing on Smack
Cuz the attack
On her heart, post her own brother's gun down
Was greater than her lack
And now we sisters ain't got nobody left
Just broke just black just bereft
Think on this Sis
Because we are Black women
We ain't got no voice
It don't matter what we think
What we do
How hard we work
Or how many babies we drop
We can't say ish
And if we do
We're acting like a man
Or a lez-bi-an
But certainly not a lady

Maybe
That's the world we live in
We got the right to vote
It don't mean we got the right to speak.
I'm a black woman.
On the totem pole that's next to last
And unburying E-Mem, who is last
Ain't gonna "Give us Free."

TIGS: Is that truly what you believe my sister
That we are next to last my sister
We stand on the shoulders
Of her-story
The Amazons of the Dahomey
Jamaica's Nyabinghi
The Queen called Nefertiti
Don't you know your her-story?
Long before Coretta
Rihanna
And Mama of the Obama
We were Queens
That's the her-story I claim for me
Not weakness
Not disease.

IZZY: You livin' in a fantasy
A visage in a magazine
Kinte cloth and afros tall
Angela Davis don't know it all
Like J.B. sing...
"*This is a man's world.*"
I'm woman enough to know
When to shut the hell up.

TIGS: You think you real
But your hair is as fake

As the words you mistake
For truth.

IZZY: I ain't givin' my time
For no gang-bangin' punk.
Hit me up to say goodbye
Before they shoot your black —

TIGS: Shoot?

IZZY: If tomorrow Marcellus orders them buried and you unbury the one
He gon' come fo' you somehow someway
With his metaphoric gun.
You so bad, then do it.
(She hesitates, doubtful...)

TIGS: ...I will.

(Lights change as —)

SCENE 3

(Spotlight on Marcellus, as —)

(A flurry of texts & tweets —)

CHORUS: *(Texts & tweets:)* "LATIN KINGS!" "GANGSTER DISCIPLES!" "GUN VIOLENCE SOARS!" "80 PEOPLE SHOT DEAD THIS WEEKEND!" "WTF?" "HOLY SHITBALLS!" [or "HOLY MOLY"] "COPS KILLIN' KIDS!" "KIDS KILLIN' KIDS!" "BLOODIEST WEEKEND IN CITY HISTORY!" "MARCELLUS THE MAYOR TO MAKE ANNOUNCEMENT"

(Lights rise on Marcellus in tears. With his wife, FAY. He readies himself for the press conference.)

FAY: Marcellus. Don't cry, husband.

MARCELLUS: The city is out of control.

FAY: The previous mayor. Made a mess of things. You can't clean up the world in three years. It's a lot you took on.

MARCELLUS: E-Mem and Ernesto...my own nephews...I don't know... People will expect me to have a clear stance.

FAY: And you will. Guns will not run our city.

MARCELLUS: I believe that with all my heart.

FAY: Then the people will believe you, too.

MARCELLUS: ...I don't know, Fay... What should I do?

FAY: What we talked about, of course. Issue your new law.

(Tigs arrives. The spirit of E-Mem stands near her.)

MARCELLUS: Oh, baby girl.

(He embraces her.)

I'm so sorry for your dear brothers.

E-MEM: Marcellus cryin'? For me?

TIGS: Thanks, Unc. The hurt. It's everywhere.

FAY: It sure is.

(In the background: gunshots. Silence.)

(Tigs looks to Fay...)

I've got to finish dressing the boys for their funerals. E-Mem always looked so nice in blue.

MARCELLUS: It was his favorite color.

E-MEM: How he know that?

MARCELLUS: How's the prep for the wedding coming, lovely?

TIGS: Beau's excited. Ninety percent sure we will use Germania Place for the reception.

MARCELLUS: Excellent. Glad that recommendation worked out.

TIGS: E-Mem was gonna give me away...

E-MEM: I still can give you away, sis. Just ain't nobody gon' see me.

TIGS: About the funerals...

MARCELLUS: Listen. You don't have to come to the public one if you don't want —

TIGS: Well, it's not that. E-Mem said —

MARCELLUS: That boy broke my heart —

E-MEM: Broke your heart? You thought the gun truce was a bad idea. You thought all my ideas were bad —

TIGS: That's why I'm here. All the blogs are speculatin'...you gonna bury E-Mem and Ernesto with honor.

MARCELLUS: That's right.

TIGS: I like the honor part. The burying part...it's a mistake.

MARCELLUS: Why?

TIGS: Maybe we oughta try instead to —

(E-Mem appears in her memory/present.)

TIGS & E-MEM: Unearth the truth.

MARCELLUS: Unearth the truth...it's a great campaign slogan. Are you running for office against me too?

E-MEM: Wait? What?

ERNESTO: Tol' you, hermano, you got him all wrong.

TIGS: Sweet!

E-MEM: Ask him where all these kids are getting these guns?

Ask him <u>who ordered the drive by</u>?

ERNESTO: It wasn't him, bro—

TIGS: Listen, I know you and E-Mem weren't tight but—

E-MEM: Ask him, Tigs. <u>Ask him</u>!

TIGS: Unc...?

(Silence. She falters.)

...Neh. I'm good.

MARCELLUS: Run along, love. I've got a press conference.

TIGS: Love you, Unc.

E-MEM: Wait, that's it?

MARCELLUS: Love you too, baby girl. Now, have you seen my White Sox cap?

(Tigs gives him a big hug and exits.)

(Fay reappears. Holding his White Sox cap.)

FAY: Remember. Your new law.

MARCELLUS: Yes, yes, of course.

(Gunshots. Lights change—)

SCENE 4

(Gunshots continue as—)

CHORUS:: *(Text & Twitter messages:)* "MARCELLUS PRESS CONFERENCE!" "BE THERE!" "ORGANIZE!"

"SPEAK OUT!"

(Marcellus's press conference. Newscasters. A crowd. Protest.)

(Chanting/repeating:) NO MORE GUNS!
SAVE OUR SONS!
NO MORE BLOOD!

SAVE OUR HOOD!
ALL LIVES MATTER!
ALL LIVES MATTER!
ALL LIVES MATTER!
STAND UP!

(Enter Marcellus and Fay. Cameras flash. A beat of music.)

TEA FLAKE: C'MON MARCELLUS' PEOPLE! WHAT 'CHU SAY?!
WAVE YOUR HANDS IN THE AIR!
AND WAVE 'EM UP HIGHER IF YOU DARE!
C'MON MARCELLUS' PEOPLE GATHER UP REAL NEAR
LISTEN UP TO MARVELOUS MARCELLUS DA MAN!

MARCELLUS: Thank you for coming down on this fine day!
No doubt by now you've heard the word.
A moment of silence for my two nephews
These men...
Ernesto and E-Mem
Our City's newest fallen...

(A moment of silence.)

And now...
Friends! Homies! Can you dig it?
I say can you dig it?
Ya'll ain't hearin' a brotha?
I say, ya'll ain't hearin' a brotha! Listen up!
Tea Flake, my main mama, throw me a beat!

TEA FLAKE: How 'bout a little Kirk Franklin' up in heah?

(Tea Flake plays a gospel riff ala Dr. Watts. Marcellus dons a preacher's robe.)

MARCELLUS: Don't despair good people
For our good-god City
Is ruled by what's the word?

MARCELLUS!
That's right ladies and gents
Turn to your neighbor and say "*MARCELLUS!*"

> *(They do.)*

MARCELLUS
Ain't keep his mouth shut
When lawless men be snatching your purses
MARCELLUS
Kept flappin' his lips
When lawless cops kept killin' your kids'!
If Marcellus kept his mouth shut would he be your leader?!
I say would he be your leader?!
Hells to da' naw!
Tea Flake my main mama, now that we done got the spirit
Throw me another beat!

TEA FLAKE: How 'bout a little Snoop Diggity Dawg!

> *(Tea Flake's gospel riff blends into that of a smooth hip hop flow. Marcellus dons his White Sox cap backwards and strikes a pose as a rapper circa 1980.)*

> *(Marcellus attempts to do spoken word. He performs more like William Shatner than Da' Poetry Lounge.)*

MARCELLUS: YEAH BOY.
NOW FRIENDS...
ACROSS THE WORLD THERE'S REVOLUTIONS
SOCIAL MEDIA, THEIR SOLUTION
FOR THE VOICES OF THE OPPRESSED
MARCELLUS DETESTS!

DON'T BE IN SOLIDARITY
WITH FOOLS MARCHIN' ROUND THEY TOWNS?
PULLIN' UP DEAD BODIES
LEAVIN' THEM TO BE FOUND

AND ALL THAT FOR SAID POLITICAL CHANGE?
STRANGE.
DON'T USE FOLKS' DEATHS FOR POLITICAL GAIN!

FOR E-MEM AND ERNESTO
THE SAME MANIFESTO
BOTH WILL BE BURIED IN THE GROUND
A PROPERLY GORGEOUS FUNERAL ABOUND
DOWNTOWN
TO BURY OUR DIFFERENCES
BURY THE TRUTHS
THAT SPROUTED THEIR MISCHIEF
AND KEEP MARCHIN' ON!

If anybody, gang bangers or otherwise
Unearths the bodies of these boys, where my precious lie
They gon' find themselves opposite this City's gun!
Turn to yo' neighbor and say "gun!"

> *(Reluctant, they do.)*

That is my new law!
Enjoy the fireworks, ya'll!!!
Yo.

> *(Marcellus strikes a gangster pose. Tigs is furious.)*

> *(Fireworks fire mockingly as –)*

SCENE 5

(Marcellus, Fay and Tea Flake watch the fireworks.)

MARCELLUS: *(Removing his cap:)* How'd I do?
If I had to say "ain't"
Or "listen up" one more time
I would've killed my happy self.

TEA FLAKE: Marcellus you spoke every word

Like you'd wrote it yourself.

MARCELLUS: Well, you're the great speechwriter, you should know.

FAY: The folks love the slang! So fresh. So hip. Just like on T.V.

TEA FLAKE: Well, it ain't real slang. Just a flava for da mayor.

FAY: "Flavor for the Mayor." How clever!

MARCELLUS: This new law...it will calm this city down... Won't it?

FAY: Yes. To bury those boys is to bury the hatchet.

TEA FLAKE: Let bygones be past and move on.

MARCELLUS: It's not my fault these kids
Are killing each other
I didn't put guns in their hands
The notion is absurd
I'm a father after all!

FAY: At least Ernesto "had your back" as the kids say.

MARCELLUS: He was my biggest ally in the community!
But then he had to go and get himself...

FAY: Stupid dead dumb boy —

~~**MARCELLUS:** Now that E-Mem is gone.~~
No one will challenge me anymore
When it comes to the guns, right?

FAY: They'll understand you now.
Especially with your new law.

TEA FLAKE: Yep. 'Cuz you are Marcellus da Man.

FAY: Word!

TEA FLAKE: *(Facetiously:)* Uh...word.

MARCELLUS: Is my meeting with the State Council still at three?

TEA FLAKE: Right after the funerals, sir.

FAY: Please remember to take my gift for the council head, Tea Flake.

TEA FLAKE: Droppin' off the briefcase with the prezzie, ma'am.

MARCELLUS: I'm just a pompous arrogant gnat without your smooth and thoughtful ways, wife.

FAY: It's my pleasure and duty to serve you, husband. Whatever it is you need to thrive, I humble myself to and provide.

MARCELLUS: Thank you. The people will follow my law. If they don't—

FAY: Hey, now. You can't have that talk if you are to going to be the next governor.

(Fireworks fade. Lights change as –)

SCENE 6

(Tea Flake begins to play a jazzy version of "Taps" on her harmonica.)

(The Chorus carries the bodies of Ernesto and E-Mem for their funeral.)

(The ghosts of E-Mem and Ernesto linger nearby.)

ERNESTO: Why are they all crying over you? Being between living and dead sucks.

E-MEM: You reap what you sow, bro.

ERNESTO: Now that we here, ain't we supposed to be privy to all the secrets o' life?

E-MEM: Only Spirit know. When our spirit *finally* rest, then *we* know...

(Fay and Marcellus appear. Stand over the bodies of the boys.)

(Cameras flash.)

(As the funeral begins to unfold...)

(In private conversation –)

FAY: It's a real shame this same ol' same
Kids gunning each other as if it's a game
Another "you tube" funeral
Another mp3 dirge
Now two more young men of color?
What are these kids trying to purge?
What hate did we teach them
That's now a song for their souls
Gunning and killing to patch up the holes
It's cold
This life
When you don't know love
Where did our generation fail, Marcellus?
Denying the glove?

(He says nothing.)

Poor Ernesto
Look at him gentle
Smiling
Like he lived life good and easy.
And poor E-Mem too
A boy whose name means "peace" in Ibido
And yet he lies in "pieces"
Un-neat.

(As the funeral unfolds...)

(Chorus Circle –)

CHORUS: IS IT RIGHT TO BURY THESE BOYS DEAD FROM UNKNOWN GUNS IN THE STREETS?

CHORUS 1: ERNESTO DID NOT DESERVE VIOLENT DEATH

CHORUS 2: NO ONE DOES.

CHORUS 1: WHAT HE STOOD FOR

CHORUS 4: MISCHIEF. MALICE

CHORUS 1: DESERVES TO BE BURIED

CHORUS: GONE.

CHORUS 2: BUT E-MEM...WAS GOOD.

CHORUS: A LEADER.

CHORUS 1: A YOUNG FRED HAMPTON

CHORUS 4: OR HUEY P

CHORUS 1: THEY CALLED THEM GANGSTERS TOO.

CHORUS 2: BUT CALLING A GANG TRUCE WAS E-MEM'S DREAM.

CHORUS 1: THAT'S WHY THE TWO BROTHERS WERE MEETING THAT DAY

CHORUS 4: E-MEM HAD A PLAN TO END THE MADNESS AT BAY...

CHORUS 1: STILL, SEEMS WRONG TO BURY THAT BOY.

CHORUS 2: WITHOUT FIGURING OUT WHAT'S CAUSING THE PROBLEM

CHORUS 1: WE DON'T NEED RIBBONS AND BALLOONS

CHORUS 4: WHEN THE REASONS FOR KILLER CHILDREN WITH GUNS GO FREE

CHORUS: WHERE DID THIS EGO COME FROM THAT WON'T ALLOW YOU REPRIEVE?

MARCELLUS: I never liked E.
Even as a boy
Every time Beau'd play with him
He'd come home
Cursing and talking
Like he was raised in the gutter.
Why do these kids think it is okay
To walk around with their pants
Hanging below their butts
And talking
Like they don't have an education?
I got smacked
Every time I even thought about
Using the word
"Ain't."

FAY: We were a different generation...

CHORUS: ARE YOU BURYING THESE BOYS
FOR THE SAKE OF SENSATION?

MARCELLUS: I'm not having this altercation—

CHORUS: OR TO BOOST UP YOUR RATINGS?

MARCELLUS: I loved my nephews!

CHORUS: BUT SOMETHING ISN'T RIGHT.
AT LEAST DON'T BURY E-MEM WITHOUT KNOWING THE BLACK AND WHITE

MARCELLUS: It is right to bury these boys
That'll teach the young kids to bury the hatchet

To stop killing each other
And let bygones be past
Proper law, wife, is that you earth the dead.

CHORUS: OR UN-EARTH THE TRUTH
THE ANCESTORS WOULD AGREE.

FAY: I hope your law doesn't fuel the gang wars—

MARCELLUS: Wife—

CHORUS: CAUSE WE WILL CRY FOR OUR BROTHER'S TRUTH
WE WANT TO KNOW
WHERE THE GUNS ARE COMING FROM
THAT ARE KILLING OUR GOOD YOUNG BROTHERS
AND WHY.

FAY: I hope they won't cry for his death to be avenged—

MARCELLUS: Wife!

FAY: —Re-venged!

MARCELLUS: —These kids are in gangs!
No pangs of righteousness
They hang-glide with fangs!
Killing each other—is in their blood!

FAY: Marcellus!

MARCELLUS: ...Forgive me.
I'm doing the best I can.
It's just a lot of stress
A lot of duress
I'm trying to juggle a lot
And not
Fall apart with so little rest.

   (Silence.)

FAY: Forgive me, husband. I don't mean to add to the mess...
It's time
Pay your respects...

> *(Tea Flake gives Marcellus a bucket of dirt. He scoops one handful, and pours it gently over Ernesto's body.)*

> *(Spirit hovers over Ernesto's body. Performs the proper rituals, sending his ghost back to its spiritual home.)*

> *(Ernesto's shoes melt into the ground.)*

> *(At this moment, the truth of spirit is revealed to Ernesto.)*

ERNESTO: Say, hermano! You were right! I know the truth!

E-MEM: Please tell me, brothuh, tell me I'm right about Marcellus!

ERNESTO: Adiós!

> *(Marcellus scoops a second handful, and pours it gently over E-Mem's body.)*

> *(Spirit hovers over E-Mem's shoes. And tries to perform the proper rituals. But she is frozen.)*

E-MEM: ...Still got work to do.

> *(E-Mem's shoes are buried, but his ghost remains beside the grave.)*

MARCELLUS: It's my law

~~**FAY:** And Marcellus' law is right.~~

CHORUS: LET'S HOPE THE PRECIOUS ANCESTORS AND MAMA GOD AGREE...

> *(Lights –)*

SCENE 7

> *(Tigs enters. She rushes to the shoes of E-Mem, his ghost lingers near.)*

E-MEM: Tigs! Sweet sister, I know you'd come!

(She attempts to brush off the dirt but it is etched into his skin.)

Dirt's inside my skin! Spirit! Help us!

(Spirit, still frozen from being unable to perform the ritual begins to cry in exasperation.)

Don't cry, Spirit!

(Her tears flow becoming rain drizzling from the sky.)

It's raining? But how? Spirit's tears?

(The rain loosens the dirt, allowing Tigs to unearth her dead brother.)

I'm free!

(She says a prayer, then she takes off running with her brother's ghost, E-Mem, by her side.)

(Enter LE ROI. He sees the removed dirt and immediately begins piling clumps of soil onto E-Mem's shoes. This forces the ghost of E-Mem to return to the grave.)

(Lights –)

SCENE 8

(Marcellus, Fay, Le Roi, Chorus.)

LE ROI: Look, man.
I ain't gonna pretend I rushed to get here
'Cause, well...I didn't
Every time I thought about what I gotta say
I said, shoot, why I gotta be the one to tell?
And then I thought, shoot, if I don't tell
Marcellus
Gon' have my damn butt
On a platter
Splattered

With apple butter and coke
So I argues wit myself
"Self, what you gon' do?"
"Well, Self, I don't even be knowin'"
"Well, Self, if you don't tell Ol' Marcellus
He gon' kill your black butt
And you got kids to feed
And etcetera etcetera etcetera"
So Self said, "Shoot, I betta tell."
So here I be
I figure the worst that can happen
Is what already gon' happen
Cause "Everythang is Everythang" as Lauren Hill crooned
Once upon Duran Duran's "New Moon on Monday."

MARCELLUS: What is your problem?

LE ROI: Listen Mack.
I ain't do it.
My name Bennet
I ain't in it.
My name Chuck
I don't know what up
Etcetera etcetera.
I ain't see who done did it, neither.
You know what I'm sayin' bruh?

MARCELLUS: Your news is bad?

LE ROI: Yup.
And bad news be hard to tell
You know, Mack?

MARCELLUS: Spit it out, Mack!

LE ROI: Somebody cleaned the dirt off Ol' dead E-Mem.

MARCELLUS: Say what?

LE ROI: And threw the naked butt under the "EL" train tracks—

MARCELLUS: What are you saying?

LE ROI: I don't even be knowin'.
Whoever did it, who by the way I don't be knowin' who it was
Left no hint or sign.
No shovel
No bucket
Not even a spoon.
Just went away in the night
Like the Phantom of the Opera or some ish.
Then the morning guard showed it to us.
We got sckared, cause it lookeded like somebody tryin' to spook a spook
Like somebody was sckared if they didn't unearth Ol' E
There was gon' be some curse on the body
Or the family
Or some ish.
It was an unearthing down with sendin' some fool home to Spirit
Nah what I mean?
Then we, the guards, started accusin' each other, like, "It was you, man, wuzn't it?" "Naw, dude, it wuzn't me, it was the chubby chaser."
"Naw, man, it wuzn't me either, it was the funny lookin' one with the messed up fade." "Naw, it wuzn't me, man,"
I screamed
"Not my butt, I got kids to feed and etcetera etcetera etcetera"
Then one guard said
"Well, we gotta tell Boss-cellus"
We drew straws to see who would bring the news.
So here I be.
I ain't welcomed.

I don't wanna be here.
You remember that song from "The Wiz"?
"DON'T NOBODY WANNA BE BRINGIN' NO BAD NEWS?"
I brangs da truth.

FAY: You think the ancestors had to do with this mischief?

MARCELLUS: God and the ancestors
Don't have time to worry about some dead boy
Whoever has cleaned the dirt off that...boy
Must be one of his 'Sciple Gangsta "homies."

Le Roi? You'd better find those "homies"
Or I will have you on a platter
Splattered
With apple butter
And syrup—!

LE ROI: Coke—

MARCELLUS: Whatever!

LE ROI: Don't worry, we gon' find them then, Bossman.

Cause I got kids to feed and etcetera—

MARCELLUS: Etcetera etcetera—

LE ROI: And.
But one thang's fo' sho.
I ain't comin' here no more.
~~The ancestors, sho' got a killer sense o' humor!~~
Um, no pun intended.
Tellin' the truth could get a brotha kilt!

    (Le Roi exits.)

MARCELLUS: Dammit, Fay.

FAY: Calm down, husband.

MARCELLUS: The people...they're going against my word!

(Lights change –)

SCENE 9

(Le Roi motions the Chorus, as warring gangs, to finish burying E-Mem's shoes.)

LE ROI: Get E-Mem buried NOW!

(CHOCOLATE BOY enters and trips over a trash bin. Immediately she grabs a stick to defend herself. No one in sight, so she starts to hit the can, a rhythm develops. BRACE, a Latin King enters. They eye each other with daggers in their eyes.)

CHOCOLATE BOY: Discipo!

(Chocolate Boy makes a Disciple pitchfork gang sign with her hands.)

BRACE: Latin King Killas!

(Brace does the Latin King gang call.)

Ah ah! Ah ah! Ah ah!

LE ROI: Shut up and do your job!

CHOCOLATE BOY: WASSUP LATIN KILLAS YOU KILT OUR BOY –

BRACE: YO, MAN, AIN'T KILT YOUR HOMIE
YOU KILT OURS, BROTHER, DON'T BE COY –

CHOCOLATE BOY: WE AIN'T WIT THAT DRIVE BY, YO!

BRACE: THAT AIN'T THE TRUTH BRO
HOW WE GON' KNOW, BRO?
ESE, WE WASN'T IN IT NEITHER
WE AIN'T KILL HIM
AIN'T THE VILLAIN
WHY YOU FRONTIN' US?

CHOCOLATE BOY: CUZ YOU AND MARCELLUS' CNN

THAT'S "<u>C</u>ONSTANTLY <u>N</u>EGATIVE <u>N</u>EWS" TO US
ON THE HUNT FOR US
WON'T TRUST US/TRYIN' TA BUST US/ALWAYS UP AND
TRYIN' TO PUNK US
TRYIN' TO MAKE IT LOOK LIKE
WE KILLAS OF WHAT'S RIGHT

BRACE: WHAT'S RIGHT?
AIN'T RIGHT THAT WE BOTH TAKE THE RAP
AIN'T RIGHT THAT THEY COVER UP THE PROB' AND
THAT'S THAT?
MAKE YOU WANNA FIGHT—

CHOCOLATE BOY: WANNA KILL
WANNA SWALLOW A PILL
BLAME US 'SCIPLES AND KINGS?
MARCELLUS' NEED TO CHILL!
'SCIPLES AND—!

BRACE: LATIN KINGS—!

CHOCOLATE BOY: BLAMED FOR ALL THE MAYHEM
STILL!

BRACE: WE AIN'T GO CREEPIN'/CREEPIN'
DIDN'T GO CHEATIN'/CHEATIN'
OUR SOLDIERS DISSED!
DISSED
LET THEM REST!
REST
THEY WAS OUR BEST
YES!
FALLEN LIONS IN THEIR LAIR!
THE MAYOR
A BOLD LIE!

CHOCOLATE BOY: MARCELLUS' KILT OUR E-MEM
AND ERNESTO TOO ON THE SLY!

I AIN'T HIGH
I KNOWS THE TRUTH
THAT'S THE WAY IT WENT DOWN
MARCELLUS' KILT BOTH OUR BROS!
AND WE GOTTA DO SUMPEN
'BOUT IT NOW.
GOTTA SHOUT IT OUT
TELL THE TRUTH ABOUT
HOW IT ALL WENT DOWN!
HOW WE GON' GET MARCELLUS?

CHORUS: TAKE DOWN CITY-TOWN!

LE ROI: This is a job and you gotta do it much less.
'Sciples and Kings? C'mon na' and do this!
Fo' I put ma foot up yo' butts—!

CHORUS: *(Whispering:)* TAKE.
CITY.
OUT.
OUT.
...OUT.

> *(Le Roi directs the warring chorus to pile even more dirt on the body. They do. Le Roi is satisfied and exits.)*

> *(Chocolate Boy and Brace both take out their guns.)*

CHOCOLATE BOY: Discipo!

BRACE: Latin King Killas!
Ah ah! Ah ah! Ah ah!

> *(The gangs race off.)*

> *(A barrage of gunshots.)*

> *(Deafening. A war.)*

CHORUS: *(Texts & tweets:)* "CITY UNDER SIEGE!" "GANGS TAKING CITY HOSTAGE" "180 PEOPLE SHOT!" "STAY IN

YOUR HOMES!" "CITY AT WAR!"

SCENE 10

(Again, Tigs attempts to uncover E-Mem's shoes, this time more feverishly and defiant, but to no avail.)

E-MEM: You're back!

(She attempts to brush off the dirt but it is etched into his skin.)

Dirt's inside my skin again!

(Spirit cries again in her agony causing a typhoon.)

Spirit havin' a tantrum? A typhoon? So much water!

(The Chorus [as a typhoon] wash and lift the E-Mem's shoes, as his ghost is once again freed.)

Free! Again!

TIGS: Take E-Mem's shoes... To City Hall!

(The Chorus [as typhoon] wash E-Mem's shoes up on the steps of city hall.)

(Lights as —)

SCENE 11

(Le Roi appears in the darkness from amidst the Chorus.)

LE ROI: Hands up!

TIGS: Don't shoot!

(He stalks her carefully, then grabs Tigs.)

LE ROI: They gonna give me the <u>Noble</u> Prize for catchin' you—!

TIGS: Not "No-BLE" it's "No-BELL", you dummy —

LE ROI: Irregardless!

TIGS: That ain't a word either!

LE ROI: Is so, you hooded hoodlum! You saggy pants wearin', gang-bang havin', Republican hatin' — !

TIGS: Let go! Let go o'me — !

(Tigs' hood falls off. Revealing her face.)

LE ROI: Tigs? Tigs? ...Uh oh.

(Lights.)

SCENE 12

(Hearing the barrage of gunfire —)

MARCELLUS: What is going on out there in my city?

(Le Roi enters, bringing Tigs to Marcellus and Fay.)

LE ROI: Here's the girl who did it!
We caught her
Unearthin' Ol' naked E-Mem.

MARCELLUS: Tigs?
Breaking my law?

LE ROI: A brotha should never try and predict the future.
'Cause earlier today I said
"I ain't comin' back here no mo'."
And yet here I be.
But this time, I done brought the girl who unearthed Ol' E!
I tol' you I ain't do it, Boss-cellus.
Tol' you you was my ace boon coon!
And now I am "free at last, free at last, thank God all mighty..."
Etcetera etcetera and —

MARCELLUS: How did you catch her?

LE ROI: Ain't you hear a brother?
Quote
"We caught her unearthin' Ol' naked E-Mem,"
End quote.

MARCELLUS: You know what you're saying, man?

LE ROI: Yeah
That I ain't do it.

MARCELLUS: Surely you didn't do

What this fool claims you've done—
Wait, don't answer that yet—
Out, Le Roi.

LE ROI: Peace out, dude. Cause I tol' ya—

MARCELLUS: Out!

LE ROI: Buh bye.

(Le Roi exits.)

MARCELLUS: Well?

TIGS: I did it.

MARCELLUS: ...The press, thankfully, are unaware yet of your mischief...
Let's just forget this happened
Run along baby girl, and, oh, can you remind Beau
To meet me for lunch tomorrow?

TIGS: No!
I will not "run along."
And I ain't yo' "baby girl"
This song ain't ending
I did a crime
So stop pretending—!

MARCELLUS: Yes, you broke my law but...I've got other things to tend—

TIGS: Tend to me! What you gon' do?

MARCELLUS: Calm down, girl.
We can fix this anew—

TIGS: I just unburied my brotha!
Look at his neked flesh and see how you
Brush all our city's truths under the rug!

MARCELLUS: I gave my son permission to marry you.
Gave you a referral for the most sought after hall for your wedding
Gave your brothers an honorable burial, even the one I didn't like
And you disrespect me!

TIGS: Why didn't you listen to me, Uncle? I came to you on bended knee.

MARCELLUS: I did listen.
Your precious E-Mem's gang killed Ernesto
Your precious E-Mem told the entire city
That I give guns to children
To toy with and play
That I profit from their bloodshed
The notion is absurd
I am a father after all!
And still I honored him.

TIGS: Unc. You dis-honor him.
Can't bury the good one
Without knowing how and why he died.

MARCELLUS: We know how he died!
You hear those gunshots?
Now because of E-Mem's drive-by
The gangs have taken over!
You slap Ernesto in the face
With your misplaced
Disgrace
And he wouldn't like that.

TIGS: Ernesto is laid

In the staid
Of the ground
In the most proper of ways
So how would you know what he'd like?
You got telecommunications with the dead?

MARCELLUS: I am right.

TIGS: It ain't about you.
The good can't be treated like the bad.
I bet other folks think what I did was right
And they would prolly tell you to your face
If they wasn't so scared of you and your law
They got different laws upstairs
Than the one's you make
You know more than them?

MARCELLUS: Yes.

TIGS: Mama God don't like ugly, Marcellus.

(*Silence. This burns him.*)

MARCELLUS: That's it!
Le Roi!?
Take this frantic child!

(*Le Roi reenters.*)

LE ROI: An' do what with her, suh?
You know what the peepas are 'xpectin'
You got tuh bees yo' word —

TEA FLAKE: "Anybody disobey yo' word gon' find themselves opposite this city's gun." That's what I wrote. And that's what you said —

FAY: Husband, surely you will spare your own blood from the consequences of breaking your new law?

TIGS: Kill me. Then kill me.

(Silence. Old Blind Woman emerges from the Chorus.)

OLD BLIND WOMAN: If you kill Tigs
Making her X-ti-Gone
Beau won't live long either.
Is that yo' new word?
That Tigs is dead?

MARCELLUS: ...Yes. ...Kill her.

TEA FLAKE: Marcellus's new law: Tigs is X-Ti-Gone now!

(Le Roi struggles with Tigs.)

OLD BLIND WOMAN: Mama God gon' get chu. *(To Fay:)* And you too, Missy.

(Marcellus exits. Fay follows.)

(Lights –)

SCENE 13

(Tigs in cuffs, is guarded by Le Roi and Tea Flake.)

TIGS: Blessed are they
Whose days are free of Sin.
No single soul can begin
Livin'
Who are steepled and people'd
In blood called Winnin'.

Poor Marcellus...

It's a lot of crazy in this world
There are the folks that love to hate and hate to love
Steady tryin' to tell you how to live from above
Takin' over startin' over cause it's the thrill of the kill
Killin' wo-man cause Marcellus da Man must hate mostly himself _and_
The Mama that be his homeland.

He destroyin' wetlands
And icelands and sand lands creatin' candy-less lands

He send my death to every coroner of the earth
To kill himself
So that he may reign and rain more dirt.

I am The Amazons of the Dahomey
Jamaica's Nyabinghi
The Queen called Nefertiti
Coretta
Rihanna
And Mama Obama's legacy
And if I stand still
I'm also Mamie Till

Not X'ed.
Not X'ed
Not X'ed —

>   *(Chorus leads Tigs off.)*

>   *(Gunshots continue as...)*

SCENE 14

(Lights rise on City Hall.)

(Piles of dead children's shoes of all sizes litter the steps, a Holocaust of shoes.)

(Tea Flake enters as the Chorus [as workers] create work song rhythms with their hands and feet cleaning up the piles of shoes.)

(Spirit dances.)

TEA FLAKE: POOR FOLKS ALL OVER TOWN
BUILDING ON XTIGONE'S FROWN
UNBURYIN' THEIR DEAD
WHERE MARCELLUS' STEPS LEAD
CITY HALL!

FILLED WITH PO' DEAD CHIL'RENS EVERY NIGHT
CITY HALL
IN PROTEST CAUSE FOLKS THINK THAT TIGS IS RIGHT

CHORUS 1: HERE LIES JESUS MARTINEZ
A GO-GETTER 8-YEAR-OLD BOY
I REMEMBER HIS RIDICULOUS MURDER
WITH A GUN THAT WASN'T A TOY

CHORUS 2: HERE LIES MARITZA JOHNSON
A LONG-HAIRED 12-YEAR-OLD GIRL
FIRST SHE WAS RAPED THEN STRANGLED
WITH HER LOCKS THAT WERE SO NEATLY CURLED

CHORUS 4: HERE LIES LASHANDA JONES
SHE WENT TO SIMEON HIGH
NEVER MADE IT TO THE DANCE
"NEVER CAN SAY GOODBYE"

CHORUS 1: ALL THESE FOLKS BODIES HERE —

CHORUS 2: PUT HERE BY FOLKS THEY LOVED —

CHORUS 4: TRYIN' TO DO WHAT'S RIGHT FOR THIS CITY —

CHORUS 1: LEAD BY SPIRIT UP ABOVE.

TEA FLAKE: EVERY MORNING MORE AND MORE BODIES
SAYIN' TIGS IS RIGHT
WE'RE A CITY UNDER DURESS FOR HER NOT GIVING UP HER FIGHT.
FOLKS ALWAYS QUICK TO WAR
ESPECIALLY WHEN THEY'RE POOR
THERE'S GOTTA BE A BETTER WAY
THAN BODIES DEAD AT CITY HALL'S DOOR.

LE ROI: THAT'S ENOUGH!

(Deafening gun fire as –)

SCENE 15

(Lights up on Marcellus and Beau in Marcellus's chamber.)

BEAU: Pops? What happened?

MARCELLUS: Beau
My son
Are you angry with me?

BEAU: Yo, Pops, I'm your son.

MARCELLUS: You know I love your girl, Beau
But...I have to make an example of her
There had to be a consequence
For her breaking my law
The gangs are taking over
Folks are piling up their dead
On my City Hall steps
I'm convinced
Once she is gone
The citizens of the City will be safe.
The gangs
The violence
Will stop.
I'm convinced.

BEAU: Pops
I ain't got the skills to say
Where your words be wrong
But another dude or dudettes
Or perhaps even a whole city may know better
Now me, I listen to what other folks say
Cause...well
It's just wise, you know?
In addition to the now constant hum of the gun

I've heard folks mutterin' in alleys all over
About my girl.
If only those alleys could talk.
Pops, nothin' matters to me
Like you being cool
With your life, you know?
But you gotta know,
City be full of folks with opinions 'bout things.
Listen to what they be sayin'.
Don't be all caught up in yourself.
You know if any man alone thinks he be wise
Then Pops, he crazy
It's cool to change your mind about stuff
But to be stuck in one moment
Or one thought, ain't cool.

MARCELLUS: A man stands his ground, boy.

BEAU: And we see how that worked for Trayvon in Florida.

MARCELLUS: Like your mother always tells me, the law is what's right.

BEAU: I ain't sayin' nothin' wrong, Pops.
Just what I understand.
That's why you see all those bodies out there on your City Hall steps.
The people don't believe what you're doing is right.

MARCELLUS: This is my city.
My approval ratings are higher than ever!

BEAU: With the rich
But what about the poor?
Who are tripping over their dead kids
On their doorsteps
It's the poor
That are leavin' their dead kids at your City Hall door

Even the cops are killing kids, Pops!
This is your city?

MARCELLUS: I have been fighting for gun reform since
taking office
We're doing everything we can to enforce more gun control
laws.
Your country has the right to bear arms
The Supreme Court repealed our gun ban
Now anybody and their Mama can have a gun in our city
And yet I'm to blame for all the people being murdered?

E-MEM: Where are these kids getting these guns?

MARCELLUS: We started the churches and schools summer
program this year
And the "turn-in-your-guns" day program—

E-MEM: Where are these kids getting these guns?

MARCELLUS: You know how much it is costing my
administration
To pay people to turn in their guns?
What else do you want from me?

BEAU: Answers! Accountability!
I'm telling you
But you ain't hearin'me.

MARCELLUS: Don't you use the word "Ain't" to me boy!

BEAU: What happened to you, Pops?
You used to care about what's right
Now all you seem to favor is might.
What else is being a leader
But listenin' to what your city says
Listenin' to the Ancestors, to Mama God
Then doin' what's right?
Why *ain't* you hearin' me?

MARCELLUS: I am the Law!

BEAU: You will never be governor!

MARCELLUS: And you will never marry that girl!

BEAU: What?

MARCELLUS: Le Roi!? Bring that girl to die. Right here, right now. Before this sad little boy's eyes.

BEAU: ...Take a good look at my shoes, Pops. Where you think you'll see them next? At your City Hall's door?

MARCELLUS: You threatening me, son?

(Beau exits.)

TEA FLAKE: Your son be gone.
The man be gone.
And he's pissed off.
A man like that, all young and full of fiery spit
Can be real stupid with this kind o' ish.

MARCELLUS: He isn't a man! And he isn't going to end his life because of her...he wouldn't...would he?

FAY: These are troubled times. And he is a troubled boy. Anything is possible in this life.

MARCELLUS: ...He says I'm not listening, I'm listening. ...I won't kill her.

FAY: ...Surely, the ancestors smile now. But...well...she must be punished. You cannot risk credibility this close to the election.

MARCELLUS: Surely without you, I'd be lost.

FAY: What will you do?

MARCELLUS: ...I'll take her to the loneliest place in the world
The last remaining public housing project

I will bury her
In an elevator shaft
I will give her food
But she will have to live forever
In that dark hole
Among the piss
And the excrement
And the trash
And the rats
And the dead winos
And the ghetto kids
Who will prance by
And think she is a ghost
They will see her and understand
There is power in laying down their guns
Burying the hatchet
And letting bygones be past
There, let her do whatever the hell she wants
Let her pray to her glorious ancestors that they rescue her
sorry self —

(Lights change –)

SCENE 16

(Tigs enters with Le Roi and Chorus as guards prepare to take Tigs to the dark hole of death.)

TEA FLAKE: Love of brother, love of country
It's a strong woman who could balance the two
Serving two masters and thereby
Serving herself and her God
I look in her face
And I see the warrior queen
Unconquered, though she in chains
Free, though her soul's caged by righteousness

And anguish
And truth.
Her truth
Which I cannot agree with because I am a servant of da Man
And his wo-man
I see life in this wild child's eyes
But I see fear too...

(E-Mem's ghost watches from his grave. Spirit hovers nearby.)

I've been loyal to Marcellus.
Done everything he asked.
But now, is this cool?
Have I been a fool?
This girl is going to darkness where she's gonna die
Tigs whose fire and heat ain't let her live a lie.

TIGS: This is my last trip
Dippin' in the sun of light that's hip
Givin' my life to the dead
My head is trippin'
Ain't gon' be no double-dip
Don't get to live and bump Beau's hips
No lovin' and heat, just passioned defeat
Ain't sweet or neat, Marcellus that cheat!
The Hole in the Dark Projects gon' be my pimp

TEA FLAKE: You had yo' chance
Done made your fate
Alone your state.

E-MEM: You go to the dead
Your head full a' lead
No marriage bed
Just black instead

TIGS: ...E-Mem? Is that you?

E-MEM: You can hear me, sister?

TIGS: I must be losing my mind.

E-MEM: No sister! I'm right here!

TEA FLAKE: You don' gone to the edge
And you fallin' off, my friend
Hearin' voices in yo' head
This cause o' yo' bro'?

TIGS: *(To E-Mem:)* I'm scared
But I've fared.
My fate stuck in my throat
Coated with kinfolks that choke
I can't watch this ish
My life
no mo'.

TEA FLAKE: Watch your ish.
Like many a chick before you flicked
Their eyes and all they seen was lies.

TIGS: I'm a woman! Not somebody's chick! You hear me!?
You must only know about Marcellus
And Power
And Money
Not honey,
Not a woman whose juice is cool
~~Marcellus don't know squat about a woman who's hot~~
If he did, he'd change from being Marcellus
Cause he can
Recognize his jealous

If I lived
I could change all the Marcellus' of the world
Hurl
Them into an abyss remissed

Til they shot kids straight
From their own hip

I'm going to my hole in the projects
Think of me hangin' out there
I ain't got no fear
It ain't near
It's just me
Where ain't nobody comin' to see

E-MEM: Don't say that, sister.
I'**m** comin' to see.
Your bro forever in eternity.

TEA FLAKE: This what yo' bro leave to you?
A hole in the projects?
By your damn self?

TIGS: Tea Flake, you touched my fear...
I hurt in here, deep in my heart
How'd you know why I give it up to the dead?
And now, I gotta go to them.
My Pops, my Mama
I go to you my bro
Whose nakedness I unearthed
I go to the ancestors, to my God, my God...
O my brother! My love for you gon' rob me of my life!

TEA FLAKE: Tigs, you ain't got nobody to blame but yourself.

TIGS: I'm gon' by myself!
Don't cry for me Sarafina
Or wrap your thoughts around this fierce hyena
I don't want your sympathy
Ain't no "why me" being sung in my throat...!

I ain't never knowed a man
Ain't never heard

Ain't gon hear no wedding pomp
His words upon no wedding night
No married life
No babies...!
I walk a cold road
Untold
What's gon' unfold
Ain't no use now
Lookin' ahead
Lookin' instead
I go alone.
That black hole
In them black project homes
Gon' be my prison
Where I lose my cherry
Where I lay my breath
From there I'm gon' see my Pops
And my Mama and My bro!
My bro!
It's cause a' you that I'm gon' thru this!
This what I get for lovin' you!
But I only gave you what you had comin'.
If I'da had me some kids
Or Beau, sweet Beau in my crib,
I'd not done for them what I'm doin' for you!
What am I sayin'?
I must be crazy like Izzy said!
I could have another man
Another man
But when Mama and Pops died
Can't have no other brotha
Inside me is, was...the best of black men
Men!
MARCELLUS!

He send me to my grave!
What'd I do!?
My crime was love.
Lovin' you, my brother, was my sin.
That be the law of Marcellus Da Man!

Men take me to die.
Men made the law saying I did wrong.
Men will put me in the elevator shaft in the projects.
Men take away my light.
Funny, all I did was for a man.
A man who Marcellus da Man say ain't right.

Because I ain't kill my love
My love gon' kill me.
In this world, killers of love —!

*(Ala "Summertime" from Porgy & Bess:) "AND THE LIVIN'S
EASY..."*

TIGS & E-MEM: *"...HUSH LITTLE TIGGY, DON'T YOU
CRY..."*

> *(Chorus begins to lead Tigs away.)*

TEA FLAKE: A sister trapped in the projects
Will eventually stop
Breathin'.
She ain't heavin'
No regret, only love unrealized yet
In this flesh.
A daughter trapped
Is the light, is certainly right
She the better part of Marcellus
If he'd listen
She the reason for being
If he knew who he was
When a man listens to others

He more of himself
To himself, to the world!
Not a curl on a lip
Not a hand on a hip
Not a shoulder with a chip
But a man who knows his ish.
But now he's lives in Lack
Attackin'
Hi-jackin' her spirit
For not takin' his flack.

Buried alive
Marcellus contrived.
Daughter in the darkness.
My brother and sisteren, mark this.
WILL XTIGONY DIE?

    (Lights change –)

SCENE 17

(Marcellus and Old Blind Woman led by a GANG-BANGER, played by Chorus 1. Tea Flake and Fay watch.)

OLD BLIND WOMAN: See this young ass guhl by my side?
It take huh to lead my old blind heinie
To see your dumb middle-aged heinie.

MARCELLUS: Blind Woman...
Everybody knows you are a seer
And in the past my administration has paid you well for it.
But you're not on my payroll anymore.
You're here because...why?

OLD BLIND WOMAN: I's got somethin' to say.

MARCELLUS: I've heard it before.

OLD BLIND WOMAN: Um hm.

And when you did, what have happened?
Things was good fuh yuh, wasn't they?
Your dumb ass got elected tuh mayor.

MARCELLUS: Um hm.

OLD BLIND WOMAN: So listen.
I's maybe can't see nothin' that's in front o' my crusty face
But I got ears like a war hawk
And you knows what?
Our chil'ren in a war.

MARCELLUS: I hear the constant hum of gunfire.
Tell me something I don't already know.

OLD BLIND WOMAN: I's sittin' in the light
Listenin' to the voices of the dim
Hearin' the wings of the pigeons
They was rippin' at each other in the air
I got down on my knees
Offered sacrifice
Prayer
But the ancestors and Mama God wasn't havin' it
So I asked somebody
"Tell me what's got these birds actin' all cross-eyed crazy like."
But I's know
I may be a blind old woman
But I heards what the voices say
Them pigeons is very angry wit' you and yourn

MARCELLUS: With me?

OLD BLIND WOMAN: And yourn.
You got dirt in yo' eyes so thick you cain't see?
Your blindness has poisoned this city
Yo' people done left they chilren's unearthed
Cause you let they babies be buried wit lies
Them pigeons done ate the flesh of the E-Mem

And the young layin' all ova them steps o'yo' City Hall
They tastin' and feastin' on the crusted over blood
Of all them dead chilrens.
And they's mad
Spirit been tryin' to do her thang
To send that boy on home to glory
And it ain't happenin.'

MARCELLUS: Don't tell me what to do
With that dead boy.

OLD BLIND WOMAN: Oh I'ma tell yuhs what tuh do alright.
Yuhs needs tuh uncover up yuh eyes
And see.
You wanna be gov'nor?
A true gov'nor? Leader of the people?
Hear what I says and do what I says...
Let Spirit help you open yuh eyes tuh see.

MARCELLUS: I see, old woman! You're the one who is blind!
Not me!

OLD BLIND WOMAN: Guns babysit our kids.

MARCELLUS: My kids have bodyguards.

OLD BLIND WOMAN: And ignorance babysit you.

So now God angry too.

MARCELLUS: My city is fine.

OLD BLIND WOMAN: All the streets of this city hate you
Because the pigeons and the rats
Got their baby's blood in their veins
And they carry it to every back alley corner of this
Your city
That blood's at everybody's
Little house on the South Prairie

So they's eatin' it with they microwave dinners
It's the tick and lice
In their kids' heads
And it's the poison in the pillow
Of where folks lays they heads at night—

MARCELLUS: Look, lady.
You're wise, but not on this.

OLD BLIND WOMAN: Pretty soon, your little house on the South Prairie
Gon' be filled with cries and tears of those you love.
Cause the one you love
Is doin' what you cain't
And seein' what you ain't—!

(Fay enters.)

FAY: You're upsetting my husband.

OLD BLIND WOMAN: *(To Marcellus:)* So how did yo' meetin' wit the State Council go? Did they find a suitable candidate yet tuh opposition yuh?

FAY: Please leave here.

OLD BLIND WOMAN: How'd they like yo' giff, Miss Fay?

FAY: Excuse me?

OLD BLIND WOMAN: *(To Chorus 1:)* Guhl! Take me back to the home

…And give it to me.

CHORUS 1: Give you what, old lady?

OLD BLIND WOMAN: That semi-automatic with a 30-round magazine sittin in yo' crotch.

(Chorus 1 turns over her gun.)

Somebody gotta unearth the truth!

The pigeons in the air
Tol' me you and yourn spread evil
Everywhere.
You spit on Mama God? She gon' kick yo' fanny for it!

FAY: Husband, call the guards!

MARCELLUS: GUARDS!

OLD BLIND WOMAN: I feel her. Spirit is here!

(Spirit appears. She leads the chorus in enveloping Marcellus and Fay.)

MARCELLUS: GHOSTS! I SEE ONLY GHOSTS!

FAY: NO HUSBAND, THEY AREN'T THERE—

(Chorus lifts and place Marcellus and Fay in the center of the City Hall steps amidst all the dead children's shoes.)

(A cacophony of voices –)

MARCELLUS: I ONLY HEAR THEIR VOICES OF DIM ECHOING IN MY HEAD—

FAY: DON'T LISTEN—!

(The bodies belonging to the shoes rise up, encircling them –)

CHORUS: DEANDRE BROOKS, TWO MONTHS, TIONNI GLAZBY, TWO MONTHS, MEKELA SMITH, FIVE MONTHS—

E-MEM: MEKELA WOULD ALWAYS CRY WHEN SHE WASN'T BEING HELD—

CHORUS 1: PUT THAT BOY IN THE GROUND PROPER.

MARCELLUS: BUT FRIENDS! HOMIES!

FAY: IT'S A LIE—!

CHORUS 2: MAYA FEURER, SIXTEEN MONTHS, DYMAN DAVIS, TWO, YERITZA TORRES, THREE—

E-MEM: YERITZA LOVED TO DANCE WITH HER MAMA TO JAMES BROWN —

CHORUS 3: IF TIGS IS KILLED, BEAU WON'T LIVE LONG EITHER —

MARCELLUS & FAY: MARCELLUS!

BEAU: WHAT ELSE IS BEING A LEADER BUT DOIN' WHAT'S RIGHT, YOU KNOW?

CHORUS 4: MICHAEL PADIN, FIVE, ANA MATEO, SEVEN, RENE GUILLEN, TWELVE —

E-MEM: RENE LOVED TO PLAY THE WII —

MARCELLUS: TURN TO YOUR NEIGHBOR AND SAY "MARCELLUS!"

FAY: MARCELLUS!

CHORUS 1: SO HOW DID YO' MEETIN' WIT THE STATE COUNCIL GO?

CHORUS 2: JIM ODEN III, 19, JORGE OSORIO, 19 —

CHORUS 3: DID THEY FIND A SUITABLE CANDIDATE YET TUH OPPOSITION YUH?

E-MEM: JORGE JUST RETURNED FROM IRAQ —

MARCELLUS & FAY: HELL TO THE NAW!

CHORUS 4: CHRISTIAN SIMPSON, 19 —

E-MEM: HIS GIRLFRIEND JUST GAVE BIRTH TO A SON —

BEAU: THEN KILL ME, TOO.

E-MEM: — BEAU, 19 —

MARCELLUS: I SERVED THE PEOPLE — !

FAY: YES HE DID!

CHORUS: YOU SERVED YOURSELVES!

TIGS: MAMA GOD DON'T LIKE UGLY!

E-MEM: — BEAU, 19 —

TIGS: UNEARTH THE TRUTH!

E-MEM: — BEAU LOVES HIS TIGS, 19 — !

CHORUS: UNEARTH THE TRUTH!

FAY: WHAT?

MARCELLUS: SPIRIT! HELP ME SEE...

(Marcellus collapses into tears.)

Help me...
Help me see...

(A breeze. In the voices of the wind.)

SPIRIT: Ask ya Missus to help you see! Help him see, Miss Fay!

MARCELLUS: See what, Wife?

SPIRIT: — The...children —

MARCELLUS: What children?

FAY: ...They weren't supposed to hit our children...

MARCELLUS: What?

FAY: ...The drive-by, dammit! I set it up...to fuel the gang wars and raise gun profits. Then I gave the profits as gifts to the State Council. How else could you run for office unopposed?

MARCELLUS: ...wife —

FAY: But they weren't supposed to hit our boys...

MARCELLUS: ...Wife...no...wife —

FAY: Who am I?! Some shadow? Some ghost whose shoes have been left behind? Just a Black Woman. Day after day running children to daycare and scrambling eggs. Night after night. Watching the news, listening to you bitch, everything pundits said about you coming true coming up through grass roots means and taking the political stage. Like I hadn't sat there right next to you in that damn law school. Just as easy on the eyes. With better grades. I wrote your law review essays! But wait, no power, even though I make all your decisions. No voice, even though every word you speak on the trail and in press I craft. It doesn't matter...my voice, my voice... I made you, I did. ME.

MARCELLUS: ...Spirit, help us... now...

SPIRIT: Go yourself to the projects
Where the housing projects used to be
Let Tigs go
Go yourself to the E-Mem's grave
Unearth the boy
Unearth the children that are dead
Listen to their cries
And wash them
Cleanse them
With your tears

MARCELLUS: Cleanse them with my tears.

(Marcellus exits hurriedly, leaving Fay behind. E-Mem's spirit trails after him.)

TEA FLAKE: *A CHANGE OF MIND*
A CHANGE OF HEART
ALLOW MAMA GOD COME AND DO HER PART
IS THE CHANGE OF HEART IN TIME
OR TOO LATE?

(Lights –)

SCENE 18

(Tigs tied up in the elevator shaft. Spirit lingers near by.)

TIGS: The black rats beneath my stocking-less feet comfort me
And as I hold the silk of my hosiery between my palms
Psalms don't comfort, especially of the 23
There are sighs and shouts from the drafty shaft's winds
Amidst the piss and ticks which now be my crib...
I hear the whisper of Spirit sayin' there ain't no sufferin'
And when the ticks sleep my heart be speakin' in a tongue
Which lack understandin' of their truths
She beat wild and wicked as if she done sumpen' wrong
Soon she gon' know the way of the rats swimmin' below
They whisper, "be fearless in the face of changin' currents, my sistuh
Metamorpf, become something unfamiliar to your present..."
I ain't gon' resist when my breath breathes her oxygen into the waves
When my blood flows one with them currents,
When my hands take this hosiery and transform my heart's X-ness...
Into Eternity's fleshless kind of love...

TEA FLAKE: *IS THE CHANGE OF HEART IN TIME OR TOO LATE?*

(Lights shift –)

(Marcellus at E-Mem's makeshift grave. He digs fiendishly until E-Mem's body is revealed.)

MARCELLUS: Dear E-Mem...my nephew...

(Marcellus locks eyes with E-Mem's ghost.)

E-Mem. Oh god, E-Mem...

E-MEM: What, Marcellus?

(Fay enters, hurriedly.)

MARCELLUS: Please, E-Mem, please—forgive her...forgive me...us... I'm sorry, son.

(Marcellus cries.)

E-MEM: Marcellus cries...for me.

(Spirit embraces Marcellus. She collects his tears with a bucket. Marcellus takes the bucket and pours his tears onto E-Mem's shoes, then reburies E-Mems' shoes properly. E-Mem moves in oneness with Spirit. His dance completed, Spirit hands him his shoes, he takes them, walking slowly into eternity, becoming an ancestor.)

SPIRIT: Come home, son.

TEA FLAKE: *THE CHANGE OF HEART WAS IN TIME....*

(Lights shift —)

OR TOO LATE?

(Tigs ties her hosiery around her neck and fastens them to the shaft. She jumps. Her body suspends inside the shaft.)

(Fay enters. She sees Tigs' shoes falling off her feet.)

FAY: Tigs!

(Fay cuts the hosiery, cuts down Tigs.)

No, darling—Say something—Breathe—Breathe honey, c'mon—C'mon and breathe—!

TEA FLAKE: *OR...TOO LATE?*

(Tigs appears dead.)

(Spirit begins to do her death ritual dance.)

BEAU: Tigs—

*(Beau enters. His cry stops Spirit in her tracks. He sees Fay
trying to breathe life into the body of Tigs. He pushes Fay aside,
and wraps himself around Tigs' body.)*

Your love and fiery heart
Wouldn't let you live a lie.
Now as I hold a cold you
You've decided to die.
To leave me and the promise of "we" behind.
Breathe honey, breathe.
I can't hide my regret
Can't despise of you yet.
Though I will when my blood lets
And lets
Me see your truth which gon' bind you in time
You leave me. Your nameless, unwedded one behind —
Don't you leave.
Breathe honey, breathe.

(Marcellus enters.)

MARCELLUS: Wake up, girl.

TEA FLAKE: *...IT'S TOO LATE...*

*(Spirit hovers. Ready to take Tigs home to glory. Beau cradles
her affectionately.)*

BEAU: I love you, Tiggy
My one so holy
Take your place in her-story
My lover only
In eternity...

FAY: Go on son, add her shoes to the pile.

(Beau closes her eyes.)

*(He kneels by her side to remove her remaining shoe from her
foot to add it to the pile of dead children's shoes.)*

(This action triggers her to cough. She coughs wickedly. Wildly. Like a newborn taking its first breath.)

(Spirit moves away from Tigs.)

TIGS: *(Breathing heavy:)* — I — I — I'm still here — still — here —

TEA FLAKE: The change of heart was in time.

(A car screech.)

OR TOO LATE?

(Bam! Bam! Bam! Bam!)

(An explosion of unseen gunfire.)

Drive-by! Everybody get down!

(Chaos! Screams!)

(At last, the gunfire subsides. The body of Beau. Dead. Beau's shoes appear, empty.)

(Silence.)

(Sirens. Of the Greek kind)

(A flurry of texts & Twitter tweets —)

CHORUS: *(Twitter & text messages:)* "BEAU SHOT DEAD!" "YOU HEAR?" "MARCELLUS' BOY DEAD!" "NO!" "OMG!" "WTF?"

(Text messages fly as —)

(Spirit hums, sprinkling holy water and dirt. She snaps her fingers, as —)

(Fay cradles her dead boy's shoes in her arms.)

FAY: Inside me I am welling up
With frightened whispers
From the deepest pits of my soul
Telling me to hate
Hate this life that has brought me so much joy

And so much pain
My son is dead
The son that came from my body
Who beared my heart in his chest
And my eyes
And his spirit
Which rose out of the undulation of our hips
Inside his eyes
I saw the sky
And the sun
And rain drops
That washed away all the hurts
And aches and bruises on my scarred body
And he is gone.
Never again will I stroke his head
As he lay in my lap
Or hear his laughter
Reverberate throughout my home
Or feel his breath on my neck from his boyish hugs
All that's left is his hot blood
Which grows cool by this wretched draft
Until it grows cold
And becomes forgotten by the people
Ignorantly ambling by
I am withered
And frailing
And failing
And my truth
Like my son's breath
Simply
Slowly...

(Enter Tea Flake with a briefcase. She hands it to Fay.)

TEA FLAKE: From the head of the state council. For you, ma'am.

(Fay grabs the briefcase from Tea Flake, a last ditch effort at her fallen life. But it feels strangely heavy. She opens it. It is filled with dirt, mixed with toys and children's shoes from the graves of the dead.)

(From the sky it begins to snow dirt.)

(Marcellus weeps.)

(The snow buries Beau as everyone watches. Tigs weeps. The snow covers. Burying the problem. And nothing has changed.)

(Silence.)

(Then...from the rubble...E-Mem emerges, now an Ancestor.)

TIGS: ...E-Mem?

E-MEM: Sister.

TIGS: Ancestral, Brother. I feel you here with me now. Thank you.

(She continues chanting "thank you" as she cradles Beau's dead body in her arms. E-Mem, answering his sister's gratitude, blows his breath on Marcellus and the dirt covering him miraculously clears. E-Mem lifts Marcellus out of the dirt.)

E-MEM: Uncle, there's a future, you gotta understand that.
There is now, you gotta understand that too.
There's still so much to do for the City, for the people.
Live what you are.
To be wise is to be almost happy.
Get up, Unc. You got work to do.
Here. Take my shoes.

(E-Mem hands Marcellus his shoes.)

(Marcellus ceremoniously puts them on.)

(They are a perfect fit.)

(He stands. He is just about to take a step when –)

(Blackout.)

(In the blackout:)

TIGS: Thank you.

SPIRIT: ...Thank you.

(End of play.)

The Author Speaks

What inspired you to write this play?
I was inspired to write this play because as a teen growing up in Chicago I had questions about why there was so much violence in my city every spring. Every spring I would lose a friend or would hear about someone else losing a friend. I didn't understand why. I questioned how could the Mayor let this happen? What can young people do to stop the violence? Who is responsible for the guns in my city? Why do guns continue to be poured into urban areas? Why isn't anyone doing anything to stop the influx of guns in urban areas? There must be so many guns because someone is profiting off guns. If so, who? Because I had so many questions, I decided to take these questions to the pen and write.

Was the structure or other elements of the play influenced by any other work?
Xtigone is an adaptation of Sophocles' *Antigone*. I was fortunate to be an actor in a production of *Antigone* at South Coast Repertory Company in California that used the attacks on September 11 as a backdrop to tell the story of a greedy king and how his hubris lead to the demise of his kingdom. While learning my lines one day, I had a bright idea: if this story could be used to tell this particular story, it could be used to tell a story I wanted to tell. I began my adaptation and discovered while adapting that the story I wanted to tell was about the inordinate numbers of gunned down young people in my community in Chicago. It was then that the first draft of *Xtigone* was birthed.

Have you dealt with the same theme in other works that you have written?
Other works I've written certainly tackle the themes of the political and how the personal illuminates the political.

Violence against youth and women is also a perpetual theme in my work. Another theme that is present in *Xtigone* that is also present in others of my works is the idea of ancestry influencing present day decisions of the living.

What writers have had the most profound effect on your style?
Ntozake Shange, author of *For Colored Girls Who Have Considered Suicide When the Rainbow is Enuf* has had enormous influence on my writing since I was a very young writer. Her use of poetic language and stark images is something that I've borrowed from quite frequently as I've learned to craft my own stories. Another writer who has had a profound impact on me is the author of *Native Son*, Richard Wright. Wright's use of the personal to illuminate the political drives at the very backbone and heart of my play *Xtigone*.

What do you hope to achieve with this work?
My hope is that this play will spark dialogue around the central issues of what is at the root of the systemic violence that permeates our urban centers. My hope is that people will read/view the play and ask themselves the important questions of culpability and responsibility, sparking important and life changing dialogue on how people can work together to create sustainable change in these areas. My hope is that someone will see or read the play and see themselves, something they've thought or heard about, and know that they are not alone in their struggles to understand the nature of perpetual gun violence and culture on their own psyches.

What were the biggest challenges involved in the writing of this play?
The biggest challenge in penning this script was surrendering to the story and allowing the story and the characters to dictate the direction of the play. I am a poet and I also love music and dance, and at times, I found my poetic voice and

my theatrical sensibilities overwhelming the basic drive of the script. My hope is that now there is an equal balance of these elements allowing the story to truly be driven by the text and story of these individuals dealing with this monumental problem.

What mistakes are most common in productions of your work?

Most common mistakes that occur in productions of my work are connected to my answer above. At times, people get so excited about the poetry and music and how that will combine with the text, that these elements tend to overwhelm the production, not allowing the words and characters' choices to truly drive the script. Another common mistake I've noticed is not allowing the text to breathe. The text works best when it is treated as heightened poetic language, along the lines of Shakespeare, rather than just trying to approach it with a more contemporary delivery. Along those lines, the text also works best when it is simply said rather than being embellished with emotions or histrionics. Less, in this case, is truly, more.

What inspired you to become a playwright?

I was inspired to become a playwright by my mother. When I was a child, I was constantly surrounded by her books and often found myself lost in some story or some character or some narrative. By the time I got older, my love of books became something I wanted to share more viscerally and communally with others. This desire led me to the theatre, and eventually to playwriting. By being a playwright, I get to share the intricacies of the human psyche collectively with others, and that truly inspires me.

Are any characters modeled after real life or historical figures?

Marcellus, who is the mayor in my play, is an amalgamation of several unspecified political leaders in the 20th and 21st centuries. His quest for position and honor, his ambivalence about his ability to lead, his hubris around covering his ambivalence, his policy implementations surrounding guns and gun violence, and his ultimate ignorance of how politics is controlling and cajoling his personal and political life are all stories that I have read about, witnessed, researched as I've been constructing this play, but are in no way reflective of a particular or specific political figure.

Shakespeare gave advice to the players in *Hamlet*; if you could give advice to your cast what would it be?
My advice to my cast would be to simply trust the language and tell the story. There is no need to embellish emotionally, for the words do all the work for you. The best thing a cast can do is to build the internal lives of their characters, believe every word they say, and allow that work to come through them. There is no need to push. There is no need to convince the audience that the play is important. The play is important and the words will tell the story without the actor feeling the added pressure of making sure the story speaks.

How was the first production different from the vision that you created in your mind?
The first production of the play was incredibly ambitious, paying specific attention to the theatrical elements of dance and music as storytelling agents. The team did an incredible job of investing in these elements with a cast that was incredibly enthusiastic about executing these elements. As I engaged in the process, I learned that the words and actions of the characters were actually taking a backseat to the theatrics of the production. It helped hone my vision to the idea that less truly is more, and that the more the text and the actions of the characters drive the story, the more the theatrical elements will neatly fold inside the story, driving the play to its natural and most heartfelt catharsis.

Is the play intended to be performed with a multi-ethnic cast?
Yes, the play is intended to be performed with a multi-ethnic cast. A multi-ethnic cast is not the same idea as a colorblind cast. Ideally, any race or ethnicity or gender of any of the characters should be able to be substituted for what is listed in the character description and the story should still stand on its own. A multi-ethnic cast suggests that we are viewing the play with the idea of race involved, while a colorblind cast suggests that we are not viewing this in the context of race. But in all transparency, how can we talk about urban areas and race and gender not be part of the conversation? It would be shortsighted on the part of any director or producer to not allow these elements to inform casting decisions, and to ask the tough questions of what story does it tell to tell this story with a multi-racial cast? My hope is that a director or producer will make bold choices and be fearless in the pursuit of what these choices mean in the context of this story and how that informs our perceptions of the larger questions of the play.

About the Author

Nambi E. Kelley has penned plays for Steppenwolf, Goodman Theatre, and Court Theatre in Chicago; American Blues Theatre, Health Works Theatre (Chicago), Lincoln Center in New York and internationally with LATT Children's Theatre/Unibooks Publishing Company (South Korea), Teatri Sbagliati (Italy), and The Finger Players (Singapore). Her adaptation of *Native Son* was presented to critical acclaim at Court Theatre with American Blues Theatre (co-production) and was the highest grossing production in Court Theatre's 60-year history. Professional writing affiliations include: Goodman Theatre Playwrights Unit, Steppenwolf Theatre Company New Plays Lab Playwright-In-Residence, Goodman

Theatre/Ellen Stone Belic Institute/Fellowship Recipient, Goodman Theatre Lila Wallace Fellowship, National Black Theatre Playwright in Residence (New York), La MaMa Playwrights Symposium Playwright-In-Residence, Spoleto, Italy under the tutelage of Pulitzer prize winner Lynn Nottage, Ragdale Foundation Residency Selection Committee, Ragdale Foundation Artist in Residence, HealthWorks Theatre Colonel Stanley McNeil Playwright-In-Residence, Chicago Dramatists Playwright-In-Residence, Danny Glover's Robey Theatre Co. Playwriting Lab (formerly The Blacksmyths At The Mark Taper Forum), and MPAACT Playwright-In-Residence, Chicago. She is also a professional actress, and has been on television and stages internationally and across the country. Kelley has a BFA from The Theatre School at DePaul University, and an MFA in interdisciplinary arts from Goddard College. www.nambikelley.com

About YouthPLAYS

YouthPLAYS (www.youthplays.com) is a publisher of award-winning professional dramatists and talented new discoveries, each with an original theatrical voice, and all dedicated to expanding the vocabulary of theatre for young actors and audiences. On our website you'll find one-act and full-length plays and musicals for teen and pre-teen (and even college) actors, as well as duets and monologues for competition. Many of our authors' works have been widely produced at high schools and middle schools, youth theatres and other TYA companies, both amateur and professional, as well as at elementary schools, camps, churches and other institutions serving young audiences and/or actors worldwide. Most are intended for performance by young people, while some are intended for adult actors performing for young audiences.

YouthPLAYS was co-founded by professional playwrights Jonathan Dorf and Ed Shockley. It began merely as an additional outlet to market their own works, which included a substantial body of award-winning published and unpublished plays and musicals. Those interested in their published plays were directed to the respective publishers' websites, and unpublished plays were made available in electronic form. But when they saw the desperate need for material for young actors and audiences—coupled with their experience that numerous quality plays for young people weren't finding a home—they made the decision to represent the work of other playwrights as well. Dozens and dozens of authors are now members of the YouthPLAYS family, with scripts available both electronically and in traditional acting editions. We continue to grow as we look for exciting and challenging plays and musicals for young actors and audiences.

About ProduceaPlay.com

Let's put up a play! Great idea! But producing a play takes time, energy and knowledge. While finding the necessary time and energy is up to you, ProduceaPlay.com is a website designed to assist you with that third element: knowledge.

Created by YouthPLAYS' co-founders, Jonathan Dorf and Ed Shockley, ProduceaPlay.com serves as a resource for producers at all levels as it addresses the many facets of production. As Dorf and Shockley speak from their years of experience (as playwrights, producers, directors and more), they are joined by a group of award-winning theatre professionals and experienced teachers from the world of academic theatre, all making their expertise available for free in the hope of helping this and future generations of producers, whether it's at the school or university level, or in community or professional theatres.

The site is organized into a series of major topics, each of which has its own page that delves into the subject in detail, offering suggestions and links for further information. For example, Publicity covers everything from Publicizing Auditions to How to Use Social Media to Posters to whether it's worth hiring a publicist. Casting details Where to Find the Actors, How to Evaluate a Resume, Callbacks and even Dealing with Problem Actors. You'll find guidance on your Production Timeline, The Theater Space, Picking a Play, Budget, Contracts, Rehearsing the Play, The Program, House Management, Backstage, and many other important subjects.

The site is constantly under construction, so visit often for the latest insights on play producing, and let it help make your play production dreams a reality.

More from YouthPLAYS

Roll of Thunder, Hear My Cry by Ed Shockley
Drama. 105-115 minutes. 6+ males, 4+ females (12-40 performers possible).

The gripping story of Cassie Logan's coming of age in Jim Crow Mississippi is brought to life on the stage. A cast of ten principal actors plus an expandable chorus performing in a stark setting transform this epic into an inspiring tale of hope and triumph in the face of adversity.

One Good Thing by Don Zolidis
Drama. About 120 minutes. 8-25 males, 13-30 females (22-40 performers possible).

High school senior Travis is miserable. The girl he's in love with doesn't know he exists, his dad is leaving his mom, and his older brother has been deployed to Iraq. He just wants to make it to graduation…that's easier said than done. Rebellious punk Erynne would say Travis has it easy. She's been kicked out of her house and is living in a mini-van and her boyfriend is thinking about dumping her. Even though they have class together, Travis and Erynne don't know each other. But whether they find each other will determine if they live through the night. A play about dealing with tragedy and finding the strength to survive, all in the search for just one good thing.

La Bella Cinderella by Claudia Haas
Comedy. 50-60 minutes. 3-4 females, 2-3 males (6 performers total, plus optional extras).

The Primo Pasta Players turn the Cinderella tale topsy-turvy with their own brand of zany, pasta-loving fun. Help the Players get ready for the ball, save our heroine from a wild boar, and stop the villainous clown from stealing the crown. There are opportunities to add music and dance, and in the end, silly rules the land!

Warriors by Hayley Lawson-Smith
Drama. 40-50 minutes. 4 females, 1 male.

Not every hero gets a song or the cheers of the crowd—or even acknowledgement. In Zordana's land, a hero fights bravely in the open field, destroying monsters and dark magic. In Amy's world, her hero is the sister who takes care of her. For Maddie, her hero is her brother, who may tease her mercilessly but loves her dearly. As tragedy threatens to consume their separate worlds, only in coming together can they battle back the dark.

Blood, Sweat, and Cheers by Kaci Beeler and Amy Gentry
Comedy. 85-100 minutes. 7-20 females, 3-6 males (15-30 performers possible).

Seventeen-year-old June returns to her old cheer gym, the notoriously competitive Austin Cheer Depot, after an abrupt two-year sabbatical. While some of her old teammates are happy for her return, rival and cheer captain Kennedy is not pleased. June battles her teammates, her parents, her coaches, her best friend James and herself to make it to the top...but is being the best worth losing everything?

4 A.M. by Jonathan Dorf (book) and Alison Wood (music and lyrics)
Musical. 75-80 minutes. 4+ males, 4+ females (8-40+ performers possible).

What's it like to be awake when the rest of your world is asleep? Meet early morning joggers, a lonely short-wave radio DJ, a modern Romeo and Juliet, the writer of a most unusual letter, and numerous other teen characters. Through songs, scenes and monologues, they'll survive lonely nights and sleepovers, discover whether the Monster Under the Bed is real and maybe even answer that all-important question: "Is anybody out there?"

Made in the USA
Las Vegas, NV
10 June 2021

24524965R00046